Take the lead in KS2 Reading with CGP!

These CGP Stretch 10-Minute Tests are perfect for pupils who are aiming for a top mark in the KS2 SATs — the questions are set at the level of the trickiest ones in the Reading Test.

We've included a brilliant range of challenging fiction, non-fiction and poetry texts — plus fun puzzle pages throughout the book.

All the answers are at the back, along with a handy progress chart to help keep track of their marks. Everything you need!

What CGP is all about

Our sole aim here at CGP is to produce the highest quality books — carefully written, immaculately presented and dangerously close to being funny.

Then we work our socks off to get them out to you — at the cheapest possible prices.

<u>Contents</u>

There are **6 questions** in this test.
Give yourself **10 minutes** to read the text and answer the questions.

Radio Milham — Milham Mornings

FARID *On today's show, I'm joined by Erin Tate from Greener Milham, who has put forward a proposal to create a pond in Milham Park. Erin, could you tell us about your proposal?*

ERIN I'm suggesting that we develop a state-of-the-art pond in Milham Park for the town's citizens to enjoy. Now, don't panic, listeners! I don't think we should take away the swings or the football fields — I want to put the pond on the rough terrain near the playground that's currently unoccupied.

FARID *That sounds great. Can you tell us about the benefits for Milham?*

ERIN There's a multitude of benefits. The pond will attract some fascinating wildlife to the area, such as frogs, toads and newts, which will be incredibly beneficial to our local environment. It'll also benefit the local economy — a similar project in Kimby that was completed last year has already brought hundreds of extra visitors to the town's shops and cafés. Finally, it'll be a lot of fun for the pupils of Milham Primary, who have had to fill in their school pond due to rising maintenance costs. A pond will give these pupils a chance to learn more about the natural world.

FARID *How would you address concerns about safety?*

ERIN Safety is my number one priority — for both humans and wildlife. My design includes a fence around three-quarters of the pond. This will only let little ones near a single, shallow area and it will also give the animals some privacy. That way, the pond habitat will have the best chance to flourish.

FARID *Excellent. What was the inspiration behind the proposal?*

ERIN Some of my happiest childhood memories are of looking for tadpoles in ponds. The thought of others not having similar experiences left me dismayed, but Kimby's project showed me I could make a difference.

1. Read Erin's first response.
    Does Erin think the listeners will react positively to her proposal?
    Use the text to support your answer.

    ....

    ....

    1 mark

2. Why do you think the owners of shops and cafés in Milham might
    support Erin's proposal?

    ....

    ....

    1 mark

3. What does the word *maintenance* mean in the phrase
    rising maintenance costs? Circle the correct option.

    support   **use**   **upkeep**   **building**

    1 mark

4. Read each statement and **tick** whether it is true or false.

	True	False
Erin is campaigning for a pond in Kimby.	☐	☐
The pond will make use of unused space.	☐	☐
The pond is likely to bring more wildlife to the area.	☐	☐
The design of the pond is very old fashioned.	☐	☐

    1 mark

5.   **Find** and **copy** a group of words that tells you that Erin
     has been interested in wildlife from a young age.

     ....

     ....   _____

1 mark

6.   Using your own words, summarise **three** ways that Erin has
     considered the impact of the pond on children.

     ....

     ....

     ....

     ....

     ....

     ....

     ....   _____

3 marks

END OF TEST

/ 8

?? Bonus Brainteaser

Erin Tate is very passionate about her plans for a new pond. Make a list of
all the positive adjectives that she uses when she answers Farid's questions.

There are **6 questions** in this test.
Give yourself **10 minutes** to read the text and answer the questions.

The Final Jump

Oona watched Javed complete his routine on the ice and skate back to the waiting area. She grinned and gave him a thumbs up, but inside her heart was pounding and her stomach was filled with butterflies, all vigorously flapping their wings. She closed her eyes and tried to visualise herself completing the finale of her routine — a notoriously challenging combination of leaps and spins that regularly got the better of skaters several years her senior. Her mind was blank.

Suddenly, her name boomed through the speakers. She opened her eyes, forced something resembling a smile onto her face and did her best to appear confident as she stepped onto the ice. Waving to the crowd, she drifted to the centre of the rink and assumed her starting position. Each second dragged like an hour. Finally, she heard the tinkling of piano keys and began to move.

From the crowd's perspective, Oona flowed effortlessly from one move to the next. But as the music gradually built, Oona felt the butterflies resume their furious fluttering and she feared her legs would buckle beneath her. As the music reached its climax, she flung herself into the air to begin the demanding series of moves that would make or break her performance.

Around the rink, the crowd held their breath, their eyes riveted to the small figure whirling and bounding across the glassy surface. Oona leapt off the ice for the final jump, using her momentum to spin twice in the air. As she made contact with the ice, the crowd erupted into frenzied applause.

They continued cheering until Oona came to a halt before the judges, whose faces were expressionless. A horrible hush fell over the rink, making Oona begin to wonder if she had misunderstood the crowd's response. Finally, the judges turned their paddles towards her, and Oona gasped with elation as she took in her score — four tens!

1. Look at the first paragraph.
   Does Oona expect to complete the routine successfully?
   Use the text to support your answer.

   ....

   ....

2. When does Oona begin the hardest part of her routine?

   ....

   ....

3. Why does a *horrible hush* fall over the rink?

   ....

   ....

4. What does the word *elation* mean in the text?
   Circle the correct option.

   delight   sorrow   fury   bravery

5. Read each statement and **tick** whether it is fact or opinion.

	Fact	Opinion
Oona skated immediately after Javed.	☐	☐
Oona's routine was enjoyable to watch.	☐	☐
Oona scored forty points for her routine.	☐	☐
Oona deserved to win the competition.	☐	☐

1 mark

6. Do you think the people around Oona know how she is really feeling? Give evidence from the text to support your answer.

....

....

....

....

....

....

....

3 marks

END OF TEST

/ 8

?? Bonus Brainteaser

When Oona finishes her skating performance, the judges don't give away what they think of it immediately. Explain what effect this has on the end of the story.

There are **6 questions** in this test.
Give yourself **10 minutes** to read the text and answer the questions.

'The Windmill' by Henry Wadsworth Longfellow

Behold! a giant am I!
   Aloft here in my tower,
   With my granite jaws I devour
The maize, and the wheat, and the rye,
5   And grind them into flour.

I look down over the farms;
   In the fields of grain I see
   The harvest that is to be,
And I fling to the air my arms,
10   For I know it is all for me.

I hear the sound of flails*
   Far off, from the threshing-floors**
   In barns, with their open doors,
And the wind, the wind in my sails***,
15   Louder and louder roars.

I stand here in my place,
   With my foot on the rock below,
   And whichever way it may blow
I meet it face to face,
20   As a brave man meets his foe.

And while we wrestle and strive
   My master, the miller, stands
   And feeds me with his hands;
For he knows who makes him thrive,
25   Who makes him lord of lands.

On Sundays I take my rest;
   Church-going bells begin
   Their low, melodious din;
I cross my arms on my breast,
30   And all is peace within.

* *flails* — rods used to hit crops to remove the grains

** *threshing-floor* — the place where crops are hit to remove the grains

*** sails — the windmill's blades, which turn in the wind.

1. What does the word *devour* mean in the text?
   Circle the correct option.

   (inhale)   (create)   (consume)   (drink)

   _____
   1 mark

2. *I fling to the air my arms* (line 9)
   Which part of the windmill do these words describe?

   ....
   _____
   1 mark

3. What happens in lines 21-23 of the poem? Tick **one** box.

   The miller eats food while the windmill fights the wind.   ☐

   The miller makes the windmill turn by supplying it with grain.   ☐

   The miller feeds grain into the windmill as it turns in the wind.   ☐
   _____
   1 mark

4. Who is the *lord of lands*?

   ....
   _____
   1 mark

5. How is the noise of the windmill on Sundays different to its noise during the rest of the week? Use the text to support your answer.

....

....

....

....

....

2 marks

6. The windmill is described as a *giant* (line 1).
Explain how the description of the windmill in the rest of the poem supports this idea. Mention **two** things.

....

....

....

....

....

2 marks

END OF TEST

/ 8

?? Bonus Brainteaser

The windmill believes that it's a very important figure in the countryside.
Find two examples from the poem where the poet creates this impression.

Set A: Test 5

There are **6 questions** in this test.
Give yourself **10 minutes** to read the text and answer the questions.

Advice from your Hill Rescue Volunteers

After an exceedingly damp spring, it looks like the long-awaited summer is finally upon us. At Hill Rescue, we know tourists and locals alike will be planning adventures in our mountains in response to this burst of scorching sunshine.

And we don't blame you! However, it's important to remember that, while the peaks are breathtaking, they can also be treacherous. These tips should help you stay safe while you're exploring the summits this summer.

Plan your trip in advance

- Check the weather forecast before you set out and be mindful of any active weather warnings in your area.

- Determine whether your route has any steep gradients, as these can be exhausting and will slow you down.

Wear suitable clothing

- Wearing several layers of clothing allows you to adjust your outfit — this will help you to stay comfortable if the temperature fluctuates.

- A waterproof jacket and trousers are always crucial just in case there's a sudden storm or downpour.

- Wear sturdy walking boots. Trainers won't support your ankles and hiking in them could lead to serious injuries.

- Pack gloves and a hat — these small items keep you warm if the temperature drops unexpectedly.

Pack the right supplies

- Nutrition is important — bring enough food and water to last the entire day. If you get lost in the wilderness without snacks and liquids, you could be in serious trouble.

- Pack light and only bring essential items. A first aid kit, whistle and a torch are necessary for emergencies. You should have a map and compass for navigation. Insect repellent may also be useful on some walks.

SAFETY FIRST
THE SAFE WAY IS THE BEST WAY

Think smart

Our local peaks offer a massive range of adventurous activities. However, if the weather deteriorates or the way ahead looks unsafe, turn back. There's no justification for risking your group's safety when you can always try again another day.

1. According to the text, how has the weather changed
    between the spring and the summer?

    ....

    .... _____

    1 mark

2. What does the word *treacherous* mean in the phrase
    they can also be treacherous? Circle the correct option.

    (unpredictable)   (hazardous)   (damp)   (exciting) _____

    1 mark

3. Why do you think the text starts with information about planning
    a trip and ends with information about what to do while on a walk?

    ....

    .... _____

    1 mark

4. According to the text, how can clothing help walkers to
    cope with changes in the weather? Give **two** ways.

    1)...

    ....

    2)...

    .... _____

    1 mark

5. Which of the following pieces of advice
    are given in the text? Tick **two** boxes.

    If the weather gets really bad, you shouldn't
    continue your activities in the mountains. ☐

    You should always pack insect
    repellent for every walk. ☐

    You should bring enough food
    and water to last half a day. ☐

    It's important to have a compass
    to help you follow your route. ☐

    _____
    1 mark

6. Do you think Hill Rescue like their local mountains?
    Use the text to give reasons for your answer.

    ....

    ....

    ....

    ....

    ....

    ....

    ....

    _____
    3 marks

END OF TEST

/ 8

?? Bonus Brainteaser

The Hill Rescue Volunteers use several different words for 'hills' in their advice page.
Read the text again and make a list of all the synonyms for 'hills' that you can find.

There are **6 questions** in this test.
Give yourself **10 minutes** to read the text and answer the questions.

Sacagawea — A Brief Biography

<u>Who was Sacagawea?</u>

Sacagawea was a Native American woman from the Shoshone tribe who was born around 1788, probably in modern-day Idaho, USA. She is best remembered for assisting the Americans Meriwether Lewis and William Clark on their landmark assignment, the Lewis and Clark Expedition. The only written records of Sacagawea's life are from the journals that the men on the expedition kept.

<u>What was the Lewis and Clark Expedition?</u>

In 1803, President Thomas Jefferson ordered Lewis and Clark to put together a group and make their way to the west coast of America. Their objectives included finding an accessible route across the uncharted western half of the United States and setting up trading relationships with Native American tribes along the way.

<u>How did Sacagawea help Lewis and Clark?</u>

Some people believe that Sacagawea acted as the expedition guide, but many researchers dismiss this idea. While it's possible that she suggested routes or foraged for food, her main role on the mission was to act as an interpreter, translating the Shoshone language for Lewis and Clark.

Her presence proved incredibly useful when the group had to negotiate with a group of Shoshones. In a stroke of luck, the leader of these Shoshones turned out to be Sacagawea's brother. The reunion helped the expedition group to acquire the horses that helped them to travel across the Rocky Mountains.

Her language skills weren't the only way she assisted the expedition. Her calm and courageous actions proved invaluable when the group's boat nearly capsized as they sailed up a river. She reacted by jumping into the water and retrieving books, papers and medicines that were nearly lost forever. To show their gratitude to Sacagawea, Lewis and Clark named this part of the waterway the Sacagawea River.

1.   Look at the first paragraph. Why do you think some
     details about Sacagawea's life are uncertain?

     ....

     ....

     ....
                                                                                    1 mark

2.   What does the word *landmark* tell you about how the author views
     Lewis and Clark's assignment?

     ....

     ....
                                                                                    1 mark

3.   What does the word *uncharted* suggest about the land
     that Lewis and Clark were instructed to explore?
     Tick **one** box.

     It hadn't been explored before.   ☐

     It was inhabited by Shoshone people.   ☐

     It was a very mountainous area.   ☐

     It was owned by the United States.   ☐
                                                                                    1 mark

4.   How did Lewis and Clark show their appreciation for Sacagawea?

     ....

     ....
                                                                                    1 mark

5.   Read each statement and **tick** whether it is true or false.

	True	False
Sacagawea was born in modern-day Meriwether.	☐	☐
Lewis and Clark were following Jefferson's orders.	☐	☐
The expedition's sole purpose was to promote trade.	☐	☐
The expedition crossed the Rocky Mountains.	☐	☐

_____
1 mark

6.   How was Sacagawea useful to the Lewis and Clark Expedition?
Mention **three** things.

....

....

....

....

....

....

....

_____
3 marks

END OF TEST

/ 8

?? Bonus Brainteaser

Look at the structure of the text. Why do you think the writer has used subheadings in this biography? Think about what effect they might have on the reader.

Set A: Puzzle

This puzzle is a brilliant way of practising your reading skills.

Cryptic Codes

Azrah the Adventurer needs help cracking this puzzle to unlock the door and get some treasure.

She has to find twelve missing words using the letters in the code wheel and the clues below.

Each word must contain the letter in the centre of the wheel and fit with its clue.

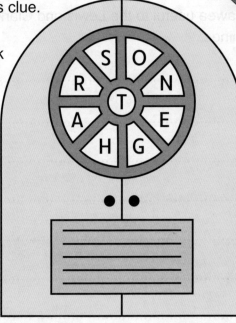

1. another word for a rock

2. a royal chair

3. a direction on a compass

4. to collect

5. truthful

6. a vow or promise

7. a spooky spirit

8. powerful; muscular

9. an additional one

10. odd; unusual

11. a spike on a plant

12. to reduce in length

1. __ __ __ __ __ __

2. __ __ __ __ __ __ __

3. __ __ __ __ __ __

4. __ __ __ __ __ __ __

5. __ __ __ __ __ __

6. __ __ __ __ __ __ __

7. __ __ __ __ __ __

8. __ __ __ __ __ __ __

9. __ __ __ __ __ __ __

10. __ __ __ __ __ __ __

11. __ __ __ __ __

12. __ __ __ __ __ __ __

End of Set A: Scoresheet

You've finished a full set of tests — well done!

Now it's time to put your scores in here
and see how you're getting on.

	Score	
Test 1		/8
Test 2		/8
Test 3		/8
Test 4		/8
Test 5		/8
Test 6		/8
Total		**/48**

Once you've got a score out of 48, check it out in the table below...

0 – 23	If you got a lot of questions wrong, don't worry. Ask an adult to help you work out the **areas** you need **more practice** on. Then have another go at **this** set of tests.
24 – 36	If you got half-marks or better, you're doing well. **Read** back over your **incorrect** answers and make sure you know **why** they're wrong. Then try the **next set** of tests.
37 – 48	Woohoo! Now have a go at the **next set** of tests — can you beat your score?

But before you do... bend your brain round this one:

Which word can be put before the words below to make three new words?

dust   gaze   fish   The word is _____

There are **6 questions** in this test.
Give yourself **10 minutes** to read the text and answer the questions.

The Pit Stop

Race day had finally arrived and the team were racked with nerves. It was their first professional race and they were the underdogs in a field of experts. Team leader Eve reminded them that they had persevered through months of meticulous preparations, and now they were ready for the challenge.

The morning passed in a blur of pre-race checks, and it wasn't long before their driver Shanice was firmly secured in her seat. Although the team shared jokes and encouraging pats on the back with Shanice, her inexperience made them feel apprehensive. Eve was determined to get her team to believe in their driver.

"Our girl looks like a winner," Eve said as the team gathered around the car.

"It's all in the leadership," Shanice grinned, "now let's do this."

As the starting flag sliced the air, the racers shot off the line. Shanice slammed the accelerator to the floor, but it wasn't enough. One, two, three cars flashed past her. Shanice kept pace with the leading pack, but it was impossible to pass them. With the pit stop looming closer, the team looked hopelessly at Eve.

"We can pull this back," she declared. "You know what to do."

The team rushed out of the garage just as Shanice's highly distinctive car rounded the corner. Soon, she was in front of them and there was no more time to think. Within seconds, tyres were replaced, the fuel tank refilled and tyre pressures checked. With an enthusiastic thumbs up, Shanice was off.

A cautious optimism began to brew as the team returned to the garage to watch the final laps. Their pit stop had been exemplary — four seconds faster than their rivals'. Those seconds made all the difference and raucous cheers erupted around the room as Shanice sped into the lead. The other cars were hot on her heels, but there was nothing they could do, and forty minutes later Shanice flew triumphantly over the line.

1. **Find** and **copy one** word from the first paragraph which suggests that the team's preparations were thorough.

   .... _____

2. Do you think the team like Shanice?
   Use evidence from the text to explain your answer.

   ....

   ....

   .... _____

   1 mark

3. How can you tell that the team were happy
   when Shanice took the lead.

   .... _____

   1 mark

4. Write the numbers 1 to 5 in the boxes to put these events
   into the right order. The first one has been done for you.

   The team carry out the pit stop. ☐

   The team check the car before the race. ☐ 1

   Eve reassures the team during the race. ☐

   Shanice takes the lead. ☐

   Shanice falls behind in the race. ☐ _____

   1 mark

5.   Read each statement and **tick** whether it is true or false.

	True	False
Shanice doesn't get a good start in the race.	☐	☐
The other teams have taken part in other races.	☐	☐
Forty minutes into the race, Eve gives a thumbs up.	☐	☐
Shanice's car looks the same as all the others.	☐	☐

_____
1 mark

6.   Why might the team have been surprised that they won the race?
Give **three** reasons.

....

....

....

....

....

....

_____
3 marks

END OF TEST

/ 8

?? Bonus Brainteaser

Do you think that Eve is an effective team leader? Do the team respond well to her leadership? Find some examples from the text to back up your opinion.

There are **7 questions** in this test.
Give yourself **10 minutes** to read the text and answer the questions.

Dear Velma,

I'm writing to express my gratitude for the wonderful job you did grooming my precious poodle Stan when we visited your salon last weekend. My brother and I love taking him for walks and frolicking in the garden, but my mum complains that Stan always comes home looking like he's been dragged through a hedge backwards. Thankfully, now we've found your salon, we have a speedy and affordable way of making sure Stan always looks immaculately clean.

From the moment we stepped into the salon, we were given a warm welcome, and we were very grateful for the complimentary tea and biscuits. We found the consultation that we had with you before the grooming very thorough and insightful. We were hesitant to bring Stan to *another* new salon but you quelled all of our concerns immediately, which reassured us that Stan was in safe hands.

Grooming Stan can be a thorny task because, although he's basically like a small horse, Stan is quite skittish. It's a real challenge wrestling him into a bubble bath, but you handled it with ease and he seemed really relaxed. He didn't even growl at the hairdryer, which is unusual! We were very impressed with how you tamed Stan's immense coat, like a gardener trimming a hedge. Now he looks like a respectable poodle, and the lovely products you used mean he also no longer has the stench of an old sock. Hopefully it won't be such an ordeal getting him to the groomers anymore.

My mum was so satisfied with the service that she is going to recommend your salon to all of her friends who have dishevelled dogs — you'll be overrun with pooches! Hopefully you'll still be able to fit us in for a return visit.

Yours faithfully,

Julien

1.   *dragged through a hedge backwards*
     What does this phrase tell you about how Stan looks?

     ....

2.   What does the word *consultation* mean in the second paragraph?
     Circle **one** option.

     (debate)   (dinner)

     (discussion)   (lesson)

3.   *Grooming Stan can be a thorny task...*
     Give **two** impressions this gives you of grooming Stan.

     1)...

     2)...

4.   Give **two** grooming treatments that Stan received at Velma's salon.

     1)...

     2)...

5.　What did Stan smell like before he visited Velma's salon?

....

6.　Read each statement and **tick** whether it is true or false.

	True	False
Stan doesn't normally like hairdryers.	☐	☐
The salon is quick but expensive.	☐	☐
Julien's mum was pleased with the salon.	☐	☐
Stan is a small dog.	☐	☐

7.　What do you think Stan's experiences with groomers have been like in the past? Explain your answer using evidence from the text.

....

....

....

END OF TEST

/ 8

?? Bonus Brainteaser

How do you think Velma might have felt when she received Julien's letter?
Read through the letter again and find evidence that supports your ideas.

There are **6 questions** in this test.
Give yourself **10 minutes** to read the text and answer the questions.

BASKETBALL TEAM PROVE CHEATS NEVER PROSPER

By Adil Alvi

A basketball game at a school in Lancashire rocked the PBL (Primary Basketball League) this week. The game, between Foxville and Moleton schools, left the league at a loss for words after Foxville were accused of cheating.

Doubts Raised

"I was instantly suspicious," explained Mr Dip, the team's coach. "One of their players looked much older than the rules allow. He was at least 6 ft tall."

Mr Dip went on to say that he couldn't confirm his suspicions, so all he could do was encourage his side to give it their all.

The Game Begins

Word spread across the school about Foxville's potentially illegal player, and when the players took to the court, large crowds gathered to see the action.

"We thought we had no chance," said year six pupil Anya. "He was just so tall."

The atmosphere among the Moleton supporters was extraordinarily tense as the half-time buzzer sounded. Foxville were winning 30-25.

"Foxville were good, but they were just relying on the tall player," Mr Dip said. "I told my team that if they worked together, they would be better than one person."

The team went out for the second half with renewed vigour, ready to challenge Foxville.

The Comeback Is On

Foxville continued their form with six points in the first five minutes. However, the tide appeared to be turning, as Moleton responded with five of their own. Soon, the points were piling up and Moleton had closed the gap, with one minute left to play.

In the last seconds of the game, Moleton took the lead for the first time, finishing with a 37-36 victory. Moleton's pupils and teachers cheered jubilantly, and ran onto the court to congratulate their team, leaving the Foxville players dejected.

The Foxville coach later admitted that they had fielded a secondary school student. They are likely to face punishment from the PBL.

1. Look at the first paragraph.
    How can you tell that people were shocked by
    what happened at the basketball match?

    ....

    ....   _____

2. Why was Mr Dip wary of one of Foxville's players?

    ....

    ....   _____

3. Which word best describes how the pupils felt about
    Moleton's chances of winning? Circle **one** option.

    optimistic   doubtful

    enthusiastic   suspicious
                                                                                            _____

4. Look at the paragraph beginning *The team went out...*
    Find and **copy one** word from this paragraph that means energy.

    ....   _____

5. Using your own words, summarise what happened in the basketball match.

....

....

....

....

2 marks

6. Explain how the atmosphere among Moleton's supporters at half-time was different to the atmosphere at the end of the game. Use the text to support your answer.

....

....

....

....

2 marks

END OF TEST

/ 8

?? Bonus Brainteaser

The last section of the article has the heading *The Comeback Is On*. Can you think of an alternative heading for the section? Explain why you have chosen it.

There are **6 questions** in this test.
Give yourself **10 minutes** to read the text and answer the questions.

The Golden Temple of Amritsar

Sikhism is one of the world's largest religions, with millions of followers worldwide. Many religions have places that are considered holy, and some worshippers travel thousands of miles to visit these pilgrimage sites. In Sikhism, one of these holy places is the Golden Temple of Amritsar.

<u>About the Temple</u>

The Golden Temple of Amritsar is in the state of Punjab in the north of India. The temple sits in the centre of a large square of buildings, surrounded by water which is believed to be holy. It is connected to the buildings by a long walkway, which many thousands of visitors walk every day. The temple's real name is Harmandir Sahib, but it's commonly known as the Golden Temple because the upper part of the building is adorned with 750 kg of gold — that's roughly the weight of a small car!

<u>The Guru Granth Sahib</u>

A version of the holy book of Sikhism, the Guru Granth Sahib, is kept in the Golden Temple. The book was created in 1708 by combining writings by various important Sikh figures with a compilation of hymns called the Adi Granth (which means 'First Book'). In a daily ceremony that starts around dawn, the Guru Granth Sahib is brought to the temple from a nearby holy building called the Akal Takht. It is then returned in another ceremony at night.

<u>One of the World's Largest Community Kitchens</u>

The temple has a large kitchen, called the langar, which can serve up to 100 000 visitors per day. The kitchen can get through a staggering amount of food — up to 1500 kg of rice and 12 000 kg of flour each day. Every visitor is welcome to a free meal, regardless of their background, faith or gender — visitors sit together on the floor and enjoy vegetarian food, served by a host of faithful volunteers.

1. According to the text, what is a pilgrimage site?

    ....

2. Look at the second paragraph.
    Which diagram best represents the location of the temple?
    Tick **one** box.

    ☐   ☐   ☐

3. *that's roughly the weight of a small car*
    Explain how this comparison helps the reader
    to imagine how much gold there is.

    ....

    ....

    ....

    ....

32

4. What does the word *compilation* mean in the third paragraph?

....

5. Read each statement and **tick** whether it is true or false.

	True	False
Amritsar is in northern India.	☐	☐
The temple's real name is Akal Takht.	☐	☐
Guru Granth Sahib means 'First Book'.	☐	☐
The langar serves free meals to visitors.	☐	☐

1 mark

6. Write down how someone visiting the temple for the first time
    might feel. Give reasons from the text to support your answer.

....

....

....

....

....

3 marks

END OF TEST

/ 8

?? Bonus Brainteaser

Read the last paragraph of the article again. What evidence is there that everyone
who visits the Golden Temple is treated with respect, no matter who they are?

There are **6 questions** in this test.
Give yourself **10 minutes** to read the text and answer the questions.

A Tasty Blast From the Past

Hi everyone, Brian here! If you haven't stumbled across my blog before, welcome! Sharing all my favourite recipes with you lovely bakers is one of my greatest passions, second only to my passion for baking.

In the spotlight today is a retro Lemon Meringue Pie recipe that I regularly made with my beloved Grandma Sue, during pleasant summers when I was young. Sadly, it's rarely on the menu in contemporary restaurants, but at least we can still make it at home!

This pie is a bit more laborious than a lot of my other recipes (and creates quite a bit of washing up if you're anything like me), but it's well worth it. A crisp, sweet pastry case, filled with tart lemon curd and topped with a billowing pillow of toasted marshmallow meringue — you won't be disappointed!

If you're strapped for time, there's the (less satisfying) option of baking some components of the pie beforehand and then throwing it together on the day. One way of doing this is to bake the pastry and leave it overnight. Some people claim this method prevents the base of the pie becoming soggy, but I personally don't find that it makes much difference. Alternatively, you can make everything but the meringue, and then add that at a later time.

However, if you really have the baking bug (and the time!), you should definitely give the all-in-one-day method a whirl. This method ensures that you can hole up in your kitchen for a few hours and truly lose yourself in the baking experience. There's also the added bonus of having a magnificent, delicious reward at the end, without all that inconvenient waiting.

Ready for the ingredients? Let's go!

1.   What is Brian's main passion?

     ....

2.   What does the word *laborious* mean in the third paragraph?
     Tick **one** box.

     exotic   ☐

     unusual   ☐

     difficult   ☐

     unpopular   ☐

3.   **Find** and **copy two** groups of words from the third paragraph
     which show that Brian believes people will be happy with the
     results of the recipe.

     1)..

     2)..

4.   Circle **one** word that best describes the type of baker Brian is.

     (lazy)   (messy)   (cautious)

     Use the text to give a reason for your answer.

     ....

     ....

     ....

5. Brian says that you can *bake the pastry and leave it overnight.*
    According to some people, how does this technique affect the pie?

    ....   _____

6. Do you think Brian has a preferred method for making the pie?
    Explain your answer using evidence from the text.

    ....

    ....

    ....

    ....

    ....

    ....

    ....   _____

END OF TEST

?? Bonus Brainteaser

Brian does an excellent job of showing how enthusiastic he is about baking.
Read the blog post again and find some examples of how Brian achieves this effect.

There are **5 questions** in this test.
Give yourself **10 minutes** to read the text and answer the questions.

An Adapted Extract from 'The Monkey's Paw' by W. W. Jacobs

Sergeant-Major Morris is telling the White family about being away in India.
He has just mentioned a monkey's paw that he brought back from his travels.

"Well, it's what you might call magic, perhaps," said the sergeant-major.

His three listeners leaned forward eagerly. The visitor absent-mindedly put his empty glass to his lips and then set it down again. His host filled it for him.

"To look at," said the sergeant-major, fumbling in his pocket, "it's just an ordinary little paw, dried like an Egyptian mummy."

He took something out of his pocket and presented it. Mrs White drew back with a grimace, but her son, Herbert, took it and examined it curiously.

"And what is there special about it?" inquired Mr White as he took it from his son, and having examined it, placed it upon the table.

"It had a spell put on it by an old fakir," said the sergeant-major, "a very holy man. He wanted to show that fate ruled people's lives, and that those who interfered with it did so to their sorrow. He put a spell on it so that three separate men could each have three wishes from it."

His manner was so impressive that his hearers were conscious that their light laughter jarred somewhat.

"Well, why don't you have three, sir?" said Herbert White, cleverly.

The soldier regarded him in the way that middle aged men regard arrogant boys.

"I have," he said, faintly, and his blotchy face whitened.

"And did you really have the three wishes granted?" asked Mrs White.

"I did," said the sergeant-major, and his glass tapped against his strong teeth.

"And has anybody else wished?" persisted the old lady.

"The first man had his three wishes. Yes," was the reply. "I don't know what the first two were, but the third was to be rid of it. That's how I got the paw."

37

1. **Find** and **copy** a group of words from the text that shows the White family is interested in the sergeant-major's story.

....

....

_____
1 mark

2. According to the text, what is a *fakir*? Tick **one** box.

a monkey's paw ☐

a sergeant-major ☐

a holy man ☐

an old spell ☐

_____
1 mark

3. Do you think that the White family believe the sergeant-major when he tells them a spell has been put on the monkey's paw?

Yes ☐   No ☐

Use the text to explain your answer.

....

....

....

....

_____
2 marks

4. How do you think the sergeant-major feels about his wishes? Use the text to explain your answer.

....

....

....

....

_____
2 marks

5. What do you think might happen next in the story?
Mention **two** things.

....

....

....

....

....

_____
2 marks

END OF TEST

/ 8

Read the story again, looking at Mrs White's behaviour. How do her feelings about the paw change? Make sure your answer includes evidence from the text.

This puzzle is a brilliant way of practising your reading skills.

Tracking the Tiger

Timmy the Tiger is missing in the forest. Inspector Ingenious is trying to find him, but she's dropped her clues and now all the words are jumbled up.

Rearrange the words to make sentences. Use them to help you number the pictures below to show the order in which Timmy visited each location.

the arguing   he passed   After the stumps   ducks

....

he went   to see   From the pond   the bear

....

the stumps   off at   He started

....

the ducks   to the pond   He moved from

....

in the hut   The bear told   go and hide   him to

....

End of Set B: Scoresheet

You've finished a full set of tests — well done!

Now it's time to put your scores in here
and see how you're getting on.

	Score	
Test 1		/8
Test 2		/8
Test 3		/8
Test 4		/8
Test 5		/8
Test 6		/8
Total		**/48**

Once you've got a score out of 48, check it out in the table below...

0 – 23	If you got a lot of questions wrong, don't worry. Ask an adult to help you work out the **areas** you need **more practice** on. Then have another go at **this** set of tests.
24 – 36	If you got half-marks or better, you're doing well. **Read** back over your **incorrect** answers and make sure you know **why** they're wrong. Then try the **next set** of tests.
37 – 48	Woohoo! Now have a go at the **next set** of tests — can you beat your score?

But before you do... bend your brain round this one:

My first is in TYRE and also in PATCH,   My third is in LEAF, but never in FLANS,
My second is in PRIEST, but not in SPITE,   My fourth is in PEACH and also in ROSE.

What am I? A __ __ __ __

There are **6 questions** in this test.
Give yourself **10 minutes** to read the text and answer the questions.

Lessons Learnt

Friday 13th February

Science was an absolute catastrophe today. We were outside examining some revolting creatures in a pond — toads, snails, beetles — when the new girl, Zola, nudged me into the water! She then had the nerve to insist it was an accident. I spent the remainder of the day with pond weed in my hair and frogspawn in my brand new shoes. She'll pay for this.

Monday 16th February

This is going to be so simple. Our class had P.E. on the field and a couple of the boys were fooling around with some worms. When Zola saw them, she made such a fuss. I was astonished at how quickly she darted towards the toilets and Marie even said she heard sobbing. It was such an overreaction, but at least I know exactly how to get my revenge now.

Thursday 19th February

Everything was going according to plan. Seeing that Miss Crane was preoccupied with a mountain of marking, I approached Zola with my jar of worms at the ready. But then calamity struck — Emre tripped me. The worms flew out of the jar and landed in my bag. I squealed and burst into tears as everyone sniggered at me. Without hesitating, I ran out of the classroom and took refuge in the toilets. I was so focused on my humiliation that I didn't notice someone following me until I heard a knock on the cubicle door. I pushed it open and Zola was on the other side. Instead of laughing at my foiled plot, she helped me pick all of the wretched worms out of my bag, even though she found them repulsive! I couldn't believe that even after my vile plan, she would be so selfless. I've never felt so guilty and ashamed as she linked her arm with mine and walked me back to class.

---

1. What does the narrator say she had to deal with on 13th February? Tick **one** box.

    A snail in her brand new shoe ☐

    Beetles in her bag ☐

    The smell of pond water on her clothes ☐

    Wet plants from the pond in her hair ☐

2. How do you think Zola feels about the worms in the second paragraph? Explain your answer using evidence from the text.

    ....

    ....

    ....

3. Why does the narrator decide to carry out her plan when she does?

    ....

    ....

4. **Find** and **copy two** words that mean disaster.

    1)...

    2)...

5.   Write the numbers 1 to 5 in the boxes to put these events from the text into the right order. The first one has been done for you.

The class have a science lesson outside.   `1`

The narrator runs to the toilet.   ☐

Emre interferes with the narrator's plan.   ☐

Zola helps the narrator.   ☐

Some boys play with worms.   ☐

_____
1 mark

6.   Explain how the narrator's opinion of Zola changes during the text. Use the text to support your answer.

....

....

....

....

_____
2 marks

END OF TEST

/ 8

?? Bonus Brainteaser

A moral is a lesson that can be learnt from a particular story or experience.
Can you think of a moral that the narrator of the story learns from her experience?

There are **6 questions** in this test.
Give yourself **10 minutes** to read the text and answer the questions.

Cosmic Celebrations

Stargazers all over the country are preparing for the
Perseid meteor shower. Louise Phillips visited astronomer
Skye Rigby to find out what all the fuss is about.

LOUISE   *Firstly, what is the Perseid meteor shower?*

SKYE   The Perseid meteor shower is a dazzling display
of meteors, or what we commonly refer to as
shooting stars. It's caused by the debris left behind
by Comet Swift-Tuttle as it makes its 133-year orbit around the Sun.
The chunks of debris disintegrate as they enter Earth's atmosphere
and burn up, emitting bright streaks of light across the sky.

LOUISE   *Amazing! When should we be rushing out to see it?*

SKYE   Fortunately, you don't have to stand by for 133 years to see it! It happens
annually from the middle of July, but the peak viewing times are likely to
occur between 9th and 14th August — on these nights, up to 100 meteors
per hour will whizz across the night sky. The meteors are observable from
about 10 pm but you can see them with the greatest clarity after midnight
and into the early hours. You might want to set an alarm!

LOUISE   *So everyone will be able to see this astonishing phenomenon?*

SKYE   Unfortunately it might be quite difficult to see the meteor shower if you
live in an urban area — light pollution can have an impact on the meteors'
visibility. Venturing to the countryside will make a huge difference if you
want to spot as many meteors as you can. I'd suggest researching local
'Dark Sky Discovery Sites', which are areas recommended by astronomers
for their low light pollution and good public access. That said, if we get the
predicted summer storms, then all this effort will be futile because our
view will be shrouded by clouds!

LOUISE   *Any other advice for a first-time Perseid watcher?*

SKYE   Yes! Take something comfy to sit on. Also, allow plenty of time —
your eyes may take up to twenty minutes to adjust to the darkness.

          Set C: Test 2

1. What does the word *disintegrate* mean in Skye's first response?

    ....

2. Why might someone choose to watch the meteor shower near the middle of August?

    ....

    ....

3. According to the text, which of the following is a feature of Dark Sky Discovery Sites?
    Tick **one** box.

    They are only open to astronomers. ☐

    They are protected by researchers. ☐

    They only have a small amount of light pollution. ☐

    There have poor public access. ☐

4. Read each statement about the Perseid meteor shower
    and **tick** whether it is true or false.

	True	False
The meteor shower occurs every year.	☐	☐
The meteors are best seen before midnight.	☐	☐
Going to the countryside doesn't make a difference.	☐	☐
Meteors are also known as shooting stars.	☐	☐

5. Why does Skye recommend that Perseid watchers should give themselves plenty of time?

....

....

6. Why might some people miss the Perseid meteor shower? Explain your answer using evidence from the text.

....

....

....

....

....

....

....

3 marks

END OF TEST

/ 8

?? Bonus Brainteaser

Louise and Skye both use language that suggests the meteor shower is incredible. Find as many words and phrases as you can that create this impression.

There are **6 questions** in this test.
Give yourself **10 minutes** to read the text and answer the questions.

The Guardians of the Tower of London

History of the Tower

The Tower of London is one of the most popular tourist destinations in London. Constructed by William the Conqueror in the 11th century, this imposing fortress has been used as a royal residence, an armoury and even a menagerie (similar to a zoo). However, its most sinister purpose was as a prison — a role so infamous that it even gave rise to the phrase 'sent to the Tower', meaning to be imprisoned. Anne Boleyn, Lady Jane Grey and Elizabeth I all spent time in the Tower, though only the latter escaped the executioner.

Protectors of the Realm

Unsurprisingly, such a formidable and impressive castle has always required plenty of protection. Since Tudor times, special guards known as Yeoman Warders or Beefeaters have worked at the Tower of London. During the reign of Charles II, some new guardians joined the Yeoman Warders at the Tower — six ravens. Charles II was allegedly told that the Tower of London would fall if the ravens ever left the castle. Not wanting to dismiss this as mere superstition, the caretakers of the Tower had measures put in place over the years to ensure that the ravens remained there, including the trimming of their flight feathers.

The Ravens Today

Currently, seven ravens guard the Tower of London — one more than is supposedly required to ensure the security of the castle. This number is set to rise as one of four chicks that hatched at the Tower on St George's Day in 2019 will soon join the feathered guard. The ravens inspire fondness among most Londoners and are admired as an iconic symbol of the Tower. However, this view of the ravens isn't shared by everyone, and a number of incidents have harmed their reputation, including the antics of a particularly mischievous raven named George who was retired to Wales after developing a taste for television aerials.

1. Which of the following is **not** mentioned in the
    text as a purpose of the Tower of London?
    Tick **one** box.

    A prison ☐

    A home for members of the royal family ☐

    A place to keep animals ☐

    A place of worship ☐

    _____
    1 mark

2. How can you tell from the text that Anne Boleyn and Lady Jane Grey
    died after being imprisoned in the Tower of London?

    ....

    ....

    ....

    ....
    _____
    1 mark

3. When did ravens become important to the Tower?

    ....   _____
    1 mark

4. Look at paragraph two.
    Find and **copy one** word which shows that it is uncertain
    what Charles II was told about the ravens.

    ....   _____
    1 mark

5. Read each statement and **tick** whether it is fact or opinion.

	Fact	Opinion
The Tower will fall if the ravens fly away.	☐	☐
The Tower is an impressive building.	☐	☐
Four raven chicks hatched in 2019.	☐	☐
Beefeaters still guard the Tower of London.	☐	☐

_____
1 mark

6. Do you think Londoners like the ravens?
    Use evidence from the text to support your answer.

....

....

....

....

....

....

....

_____
3 marks

END OF TEST

/ 8

?? Bonus Brainteaser

The text suggests that the Tower of London was an intimidating place before it became a tourist destination. Underline the adjectives that create this impression.

There are **6 questions** in this test.
Give yourself **10 minutes** to read the text and answer the questions.

The Dead Sea

"We're here," Nichol's mum announced, pulling into a parking space. Almost before the car had stopped, Nichol leapt out, fizzing with anticipation about the amazing location his mum had saved for the last hours before they flew home.

"Where is it?" he asked, his eyes darting around expectantly as he sought out the spectacular palace or fascinating archaeological site they were going to explore.

"It's right in front of you, silly — we've come to the Dead Sea!" she said excitedly.

Nichol's heart sank. No historic monuments or Roman ruins, just sand and water.

"You said this place was special," he groaned. "We can go to the beach at home!"

"There's no other beach quite like this," his mum replied. "Come and take a look."

Nichol grabbed his bag and followed his mum towards the beach, but his steps became ever more reluctant as he approached the shore. What sort of name was the Dead Sea anyway? Was the water poisonous? Was it full of giant crabs, ravenous sharks or other deadly creatures? He shuddered as he shook out his towel and resigned himself to a morning of reading about the Romans in the sun.

Before Nichol could open his book, he was hoisted into his mum's arms. He wriggled to free himself, but in a few short moments he felt the warm water lapping around him. He closed his eyes instinctively, waiting for the water to cover his head, before he realised that something utterly baffling was happening — he was floating without even trying. Perplexed, he looked at his mum, who laughed.

"It's the salt," she explained. "There's so much of it that it lifts you up. It also makes it impossible for anything to live in the water. That's why it's called the Dead Sea — it's not nearly as sinister as it sounds."

Nichol gazed dubiously at his mum. A sunny beach with no menacing creatures? It sounded too good to be true. But if it *was* true, well, maybe he wouldn't have to spend the whole morning reading his book after all...

1. Read from the start of the story to *"Come and take a look."*
   Find and **copy** a group of words where Nichol's mood changes.

   ....

   _____
   1 mark

2. Why doesn't Nichol want to swim in the sea?
   Tick **one** box.

   He left his towel in the car. ☐

   He thinks the water might be harmful. ☐

   He can see frightening sea creatures. ☐

   He wants to sunbathe instead. ☐

   _____
   1 mark

3. *ravenous sharks*
   What does the word *ravenous* mean in this phrase?

   ....

   _____
   1 mark

4. Look at the paragraph beginning *Nichol grabbed his bag...*
   Does Nichol want to spend the morning reading?
   Use evidence from the text to support your answer.

   ....

   ....

   _____
   1 mark

5. Explain how Nichol's opinion of the Dead Sea at the start of
    the story is different to his opinion of it at the end of the story.
    Use evidence from the text to support your answer.

    ....

    ....

    ....

    ....

    ....

    2 marks

6. What do you think will happen next in the story?
    Mention **two** things.

    ....

    ....

    ....

    ....

    2 marks

END OF TEST

/ 8

?? Bonus Brainteaser

Before he finds out their destination, Nichol is very excited about the surprise trip his
mum has planned. Find two verbs and one adverb which show how excited he is.

There are **6 questions** in this test.
Give yourself **10 minutes** to read the text and answer the questions.

Good Intentions

We are gathered here in this newly-built inn
To recall some truly memorable deeds
By mighty Dolores and her heroic twin,
Who earnestly sought to meet our needs.

5   When a monstrous dragon visited this very site,
Dolores and Donald were there in a flash.
Unfortunately, in the course of the fight,
Our former inn was reduced to ash.

When they feared King Tom had been spirited away,
10   They immediately sprang into action.
Regrettably, the interruption to Tom's holiday
Was a source of some dissatisfaction.

Just last week, they acted without hesitation
To banish a savage beast they'd discovered.
15   Sadly, the Gordon family's prized Alsatian
Has not yet been recovered.

In a bid to protect Farmer Olga's crops
From a plague of insatiable ants
They really pulled out all the stops
20   But somehow destroyed every one of her plants.

Dolores and Donald — who can forget
Even one of their vain interventions?
Each memory is tinged with a sense of regret,
Despite their very good intentions.

25   When the destructive duo left our land,
There was, of course, some grief,
But we also felt, on the other hand,
A sense of extreme relief.

1. Why is the inn described as *newly-built* in line 1?

   ....

   .... _____

2. *a monstrous dragon*
   What **two** impressions of the dragon does this give you?

   1)...

   2)... _____

   1 mark

3. Dolores and Donald *acted without hesitation* (line 13).
   Find and **copy two** other groups of words
   which show that they were quick to act.

   1)...

   2)... _____

   1 mark

4. Look at lines 5 to 20. What would be an appropriate
   summary of this part of the poem? Circle **one** option.

   (**Awesome achievements**)   (**Deliberate damage**)

   (**Failed feats**)   (**Stunning successes**) _____

   1 mark

5. Which of the following does the poem tell you about
   Dolores and Donald?
   Tick **one** box.

   Their holiday was interrupted by King Tom. ☐

   They helped to find a treasured pet. ☐

   They are siblings. ☐

   They pulled out all of Olga's crops. ☐

   _____
   1 mark

6. Why do you think there was both *grief* and *relief* when
   Dolores and Donald left?
   Use evidence from the text to support your answer.

   ....

   ....

   ....

   ....

   ....

   ....

   _____
   3 marks

END OF TEST

| / 8 |

?? Bonus Brainteaser

The title of this poem is 'Good Intentions'. Can you think of any other titles that the
author could have used instead? Write down as many suggestions as you can.

There are **7 questions** in this test.
Give yourself **10 minutes** to read the text and answer the questions.

How to Make a Periscope

Do you want a superpower? While no-one has mastered invisibility yet, a periscope could be a step in the right direction, letting you see things while staying hidden.

From peering over fences to peeking around corners, this clever contraption has endless uses. Its two parallel mirrors face opposite directions and are set at 45 degree angles. Light reflects off the mirrors at 90 degree angles, making a giant zigzag from the object you're looking at right into your eyes. This is incredibly useful, because it lets you see things that aren't in your direct line of sight.

These ingenious gadgets have been around for centuries. They were invaluable during the First World War because they allowed soldiers to see out of their trenches without alerting their enemies. They are also still used in some submarines to let the crew look above the surface of the water while remaining submerged. Submarine periscopes are often mounted on a base so that they can turn a full 360 degrees to see all around the vessel.

You can make your own basic periscope by following these instructions:

1. Using scissors, cut the top and bottom off an empty juice carton.

2. Place a small rectangular mirror on one side of the carton, exactly two centimetres from the bottom. Carefully draw around the mirror with a pencil and then cut away the rectangle to make a window.

3. Cut another window on the opposite side of the carton, two centimetres from the top.

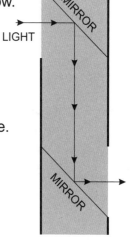

4. Insert the first mirror through the bottom window with the reflective surface facing up. Adjust its position so that it is at 45 degrees to the window, then fix it in place with sticky tape.

5. Repeat step 4, using the second mirror and the top window. The second mirror should be perfectly parallel to the first, with the reflective surface facing down.

6. That's it! You're one step closer to that superpower.

---

1. Read each statement about periscopes
   and **tick** whether it is true or false.

	True	False
They are mainly used to see hidden objects.	☐	☐
They have been around for over one hundred years.	☐	☐
Their mirrors reflect light at 360 degree angles.	☐	☐
They have been used to protect soldiers.	☐	☐

   1 mark

2. Look at the second paragraph. How does this paragraph encourage
   the reader to make their own periscope? Give **two** ways.

   ....

   ....

   ....

   2 marks

3. What does the word *invaluable* mean in the text? Circle **one** option.

unimportant	expensive
crucial	negligible

   1 mark

4. According to the text, how are periscopes adapted for use
   underwater?

   ....

   ....

   1 mark

5.   The text says you can make a basic periscope using an empty juice carton. List **three** other things you will need.

1)...

2)...

3)...

6.   **Find** and **copy three** words which suggest that it's important to be accurate when making a periscope.

1)...

2)...

3)...

7.   How does the end of the text link back to the beginning of the text?

....

....

....

END OF TEST

/ 8

?? Bonus Brainteaser

Have another look at the instructions for how to make your own periscope.
Why do you think the author has arranged the instructions in a numbered list?

Set C: Puzzle

This puzzle is a brilliant way of practising your reading skills.

Mental Exercise

Before she goes for a run, Jenna always gets warmed up with a few puzzles. Help her complete this word puzzle that stretches from her head to her toes.

You can only change one letter at a time and each word must match the definition under the box. The first word has been done for you.

LEAD
If you're winning a race, you're *in the*...

Another word for *loan*

_____
Part of a camera or a pair of glasses

HEAD

TOES

_____
You use these to write in ink

_____
These are worn around the neck

_____
These hold material when sewing

_____
Pastries that contain fruit or meat

End of Set C: Scoresheet

You've finished a full set of tests — well done!

Now it's time to put your scores in here
and see how you're getting on.

	Score	
Test 1		/8
Test 2		/8
Test 3		/8
Test 4		/8
Test 5		/8
Test 6		/8
Total		**/48**

Once you've got a score out of 48, check it out in the table below...

0 – 23	If you got a lot of questions wrong, don't worry. Ask an adult to help you work out the **areas** you need **more practice** on. Then have another go at **this** set of tests.
24 – 36	If you got half-marks or better, you're doing well. **Read** back over your **incorrect** answers and make sure you know **why** they're wrong.
37 – 48	Woohoo! You've done really well — congratulations!

One last thing... bend your brain round this one:

Circle the five-letter word hidden across two or more words in this sentence.

On safari, I saw animals, such as elephants, lions and giraffes.

Answers

Each question covers a reading element from the KS2 SATs.
These elements are indicated in brackets next to each answer.

Set A

Test 1 – Pages 2-4

1. (**1 mark**) chance (2a)

2. (**1 mark**) the Scottish moorlands (2b)

3. (**1 mark for a sensible answer**)
   e.g. shaving the edge of yawning gulfs (2g)

4. (**1 mark for a sensible answer**)
   e.g. The crew thought they were travelling inland but they weren't. (2d)

5. (**1 mark**) Laplanders (2d)

6. (**1 mark for all correct**)
   The group leave the boat. ☐2
   The roads start to worsen. ☐4
   The ponies struggle up the hill. ☐3
   The group come to a green slope. ☐5
   Hans offers to take the group on an excursion. ☐1 (2f)

7. (**1 mark for a sensible answer without supporting evidence**)
   e.g. The landscape isn't as nice in the mountains as it is at the high point.
   (**2 marks for a sensible answer with supporting evidence**)
   e.g. The high point is green, but the mountains are 'the picture of barrenness and desolation', so they aren't as nice. (2h)

BONUS BRAINTEASER
   e.g. They would probably have felt glad that their difficult journey was finally over because the text says that the roads were 'horrible'.

Test 2 – Pages 5-7

1. (**1 mark for a sensible answer**)
   e.g. No, because she tells them not to 'panic' when she explains her proposal. (2d)

2. (**1 mark for a sensible answer**)
   e.g. Because a similar project in Kimby brought lots of extra visitors to the town. (2d)

3. (**1 mark**) upkeep (2a)

4. (**1 mark for all correct**)
   Erin is campaigning for a pond in Kimby. — False
   The pond will make use of unused space. — True
   The pond is likely to bring more wildlife to the area. — True
   The design of the pond is very old fashioned. — False (2b)

5. (**1 mark**) Some of my happiest childhood memories are of looking for tadpoles (2b)

6. (**1 mark for one sensible point**)
   e.g. Erin has chosen a site that doesn't take away places for children to play, like the swings and football fields.
   (**2 marks for two sensible points**)
   e.g. She has proposed using rough terrain rather than swings and football fields likely to be used by children. One of her reasons for the proposal is so children will have the chance to learn more about the natural world.
   (**3 marks for three sensible points**)
   e.g. Erin wants to build a pond so children will get to learn more about nature. She also wants to use a site that won't take away swings and football fields for children, and she will make the pond safe for children by fencing off three-quarters of it. (2c)

BONUS BRAINTEASER
state-of-the-art, fascinating, beneficial, happiest

Test 3 – Pages 8-10

1. (**1 mark**) No — she tries to picture herself completing the routine but she can't. (2d)

2. (**1 mark**) As the music reaches its climax. (2b)

3. (**1 mark**) Everyone is waiting to see what Oona's score is. (2d)

4. (**1 mark**) delight (2a)

5. (**1 mark for all correct**)
   Oona skated immediately after Javed. — Fact

Answers

Oona's routine was enjoyable to watch. — Opinion

Oona scored forty points for her routine. — Fact

Oona deserved to win the competition. — Opinion (2d)

6. (**1 mark for a sensible answer with one piece of supporting evidence**)
e.g. People around Oona might not know how nervous she is because she grins and gives Javed a thumbs up.
(**2 marks for a sensible answer with two pieces of supporting evidence**)
e.g. People might think Oona is confident rather than nervous, because she grins at Javed and does her best to 'appear confident' when she steps onto the ice.
(**3 marks for a sensible answer with three pieces of supporting evidence**)
e.g. Javed might not know how nervous Oona is because she gives him a thumbs up. The crowd also might not be aware of Oona's nerves because she appears 'confident' as she steps onto the ice and seems to flow 'effortlessly' through her routine. (2d)

BONUS BRAINTEASER
e.g. It makes the end of the story more tense because the reader has to wait to see how Oona did in the competition.

Test 4 – Pages 11-13

1. (**1 mark**) consume (2a)

2. (**1 mark**) the windmill's sails (2d)

3. (**1 mark**) The miller feeds grain into the windmill as it turns in the wind. (2d)

4. (**1 mark**) the miller (2b)

5. (**1 mark for a sensible answer without supporting evidence**)
e.g. On Sundays the windmill is quiet, but it is loud during the rest of the week.
(**2 marks for a sensible answer with supporting evidence**)
e.g. On Sundays the windmill rests and there is 'peace' inside it, suggesting that it is quiet, but during the rest of the week the wind 'roars'

loudly in the windmill's sails. (2h)

6. (**1 mark for one sensible point**)
e.g. The windmill is described as looking 'down over the farms'. This suggests it is tall like a giant.
(**2 marks for two sensible points**)
e.g. The windmill is tall like a giant as it is described as looking 'down over the farms'. It also has 'granite jaws', which makes it sound very strong like a giant. (2d)

BONUS BRAINTEASER
e.g. The windmill thinks it's important because it says the whole harvest 'is all for me' and it makes its master 'thrive'.

Test 5 – Pages 14-16

1. (**1 mark for a sensible answer**)
e.g. The text says that it had been damp, but it is now very sunny. (2h)

2. (**1 mark**) hazardous (2a)

3. (**1 mark for a sensible answer**)
e.g. It follows the order that a person would use the information when going on a trip. (2f)

4. (**1 mark for two of the following**)
Wearing several layers of clothing means walkers can adjust to changes in temperature.
A waterproof jacket and trousers can protect walkers if it rains.
Gloves and a hat can keep walkers warm if the temperature suddenly drops. (2b)

5. (**1 mark for both correct**)
If the weather gets really bad, you shouldn't continue your activities in the mountains.
It's important to have a compass to help you follow your route. (2b)

6. (**1 mark for a sensible answer with one piece of supporting evidence**)
e.g. The volunteers like their local mountains because they describe them as 'breathtaking'.
(**2 marks for a sensible answer with two pieces of supporting evidence**)
e.g. Yes, because they say the mountains are 'breathtaking'. They also 'don't blame' people for wanting to explore them, suggesting they think the mountains are a great place to go.

Answers

(**3 marks for a sensible answer with three pieces of supporting evidence**)
e.g. The volunteers like the mountains because they say they are 'breathtaking'. They also think they're fun, because they say there's a 'massive range of adventurous activities' there and they 'don't blame' people for wanting to explore them. (2d)

BONUS BRAINTEASER
mountains, peaks, summits

Test 6 – Pages 17-19

1. (**1 mark for a sensible answer**)
e.g. The information about Sacagawea's life is from journals written during the expedition, so they only cover part of her life. (2d)

2. (**1 mark for a sensible answer**)
e.g. The author thinks it was important. (2a)

3. (**1 mark**) It hadn't been explored before. (2a)

4. (**1 mark**) They named part of a waterway after her. (2b)

5. (**1 mark for all correct**)
Sacagawea was born in modern-day Meriwether. — False
Lewis and Clark were following Jefferson's orders. — True
The expedition's sole purpose was to promote trade. — False
The expedition crossed the Rocky Mountains. — True (2b)

6. (**1 mark for one sensible point**)
e.g. She interpreted the Shoshone language.
(**2 marks for two sensible points**)
e.g. She translated the Shoshone language for Lewis and Clark. She also helped to get horses for the expedition because her brother was the leader of a group of Shoshones.
(**3 marks for three sensible points**)
e.g. Sacagawea interpreted Shoshone for the group and, because her brother was the leader of a group of Shoshones, the expedition group was able to acquire horses. She also saved some of the group's items when their boat nearly capsized. (2d)

BONUS BRAINTEASER
e.g. The subheadings split up the information in the text into smaller sections. This helps the reader know what part of Sacagawea's life each section of the biography will cover.

Puzzles – Page 20

1. STONE   2. THRONE   3. NORTH
4. GATHER   5. HONEST   6. OATH
7. GHOST   8. STRONG   9. ANOTHER
10. STRANGE   11. THORN   12. SHORTEN

Scoresheet Question – Page 21

star

Set B

Test 1 – Pages 22-24

1. (**1 mark**) meticulous (2a)

2. (**1 mark for a sensible answer**)
e.g. The team 'shared jokes and encouraging pats on the back with Shanice', which suggests that they like her. (2d)

3. (**1 mark**) Because raucous cheers erupted around the room. (2d)

4. (**1 mark for all correct**)
The team carry out the pit stop. 4
The team check the car before the race. 1
Eve reassures the team during the race. 3
Shanice takes the lead. 5
Shanice falls behind in the race. 2 (2f)

5. (**1 mark for all correct**)
Shanice doesn't get a good start in the race. — True
The other teams have taken part in other races. — True
Forty minutes into the race, Eve gives a thumbs up. — False
Shanice's car looks the same as all the others. — False (2d)

6. (**1 mark for one sensible reason**)
e.g. Because they were 'underdogs' going into the race.

Answers

(2 marks for two sensible reasons)
e.g. Because they were 'underdogs' and Shanice's inexperience made them feel 'apprehensive'.
(3 marks for three sensible reasons)
e.g. Because they were 'underdogs' and Shanice was overtaken by three cars at the start of the race. Also, Shanice's inexperience made them feel 'apprehensive'. (2d)

BONUS BRAINTEASER
e.g. Eve is a good team leader because she encourages the team even when it doesn't look like they'll win. The team respond well to this encouragement by performing a great pit stop, which helps them to win the race.

Test 2 – Pages 25-27

1. (**1 mark**) he looks messy (2a)

2. (**1 mark**) discussion (2a)

3. (**1 mark for two sensible points**)
e.g. It makes it sound like a difficult task.
It makes it sound like an unpleasant task. (2g)

4. (**1 mark for both correct**)
He was given a bubble bath.
His coat was trimmed. (2b)

5. (**1 mark**) an old sock (2b)

6. (**1 mark for all correct**)
Stan doesn't normally like hairdryers. — True
The salon is quick but expensive. — False
Julien's mum was pleased with the salon. — True
Stan is a small dog. — False (2d)

7. (**1 mark for a sensible answer without supporting evidence**)
e.g. Stan has had bad experiences with groomers in the past.
(**2 marks for a sensible answer with supporting evidence**)
e.g. Julien was 'hesitant' to bring Stan to a new salon, suggesting Stan has had bad experiences with groomers in the past. (2d)

BONUS BRAINTEASER
e.g. Velma might have felt proud, because Julien says that he was 'very impressed' with how she tamed Stan's coat.

Test 3 – Pages 28-30

1. (**1 mark for either of the following**)
The match 'rocked the PBL'.
The match 'left the league at a loss for words'.
(2d)

2. (**1 mark**) Because he looked older than PBL players are allowed to be. (2b)

3. (**1 mark**) doubtful (2d)

4. (**1 mark**) vigour (2a)

5. (**1 mark for one sensible point**)
e.g. Moleton won the game 37-36.
(**2 marks for two sensible points**)
e.g. Foxville were leading 30-25 at half-time, but Moleton made a comeback and won the game 37-36. (2c)

6. (**1 mark for a sensible answer without supporting evidence**)
e.g. At half-time the atmosphere was tense, but at the end of the game it was very happy.
(**2 marks for a sensible answer with supporting evidence**)
e.g. At half-time the atmosphere 'was extraordinarily tense'. At the end of the game, the atmosphere was more excited and happy as the crowd 'cheered jubilantly'. (2h)

BONUS BRAINTEASER
e.g. '*The Tables are Turned*' because it shows how the match changed after half-time.

Test 4 – Pages 31-33

1. (**1 mark**) A holy place which worshippers travel to. (2b)

2. (**1 mark**)

(2b)

3. (**1 mark for a sensible answer**)
e.g. The reader is likely to have an idea of how

Answers

heavy a car is, so this makes it easier for them to imagine how much gold there is. (2d)

4. (**1 mark**) collection (2a)

5. (**1 mark for all correct**)
Amritsar is in northern India. — True
The temple's real name is Akal Takht.
— False
Guru Granth Sahib means 'First Book'.
— False
The langar serves free meals to visitors.
— True (2b)

6. (**1 mark for a sensible answer with one piece of supporting evidence**)
e.g. A visitor might feel overwhelmed as they would be surrounded by thousands of people.
(**2 marks for a sensible answer with two pieces of supporting evidence**)
e.g. They might feel impressed by the temple because it is covered in so much gold and produces a large amount of food in the langar.
(**3 marks for a sensible answer with three pieces of supporting evidence**)
e.g. They might feel impressed by the temple because it is covered in gold, and because the langar prepares a 'staggering amount of food'. They might also feel cared for if they share a meal with other visitors. (2d)

BONUS BRAINTEASER
e.g. Everyone is welcome to food in the langar, no matter where they come from, what they believe in or their gender. Also, everyone sits together on the floor, which shows that everyone is treated equally.

Test 5 – Pages 34-36

1. (**1 mark**) baking (2b)

2. (**1 mark**) difficult (2a)

3. (**1 mark for both correct**)
it's well worth it
you won't be disappointed (2d)

4. (**1 mark for circling the correct answer and giving one piece of supporting evidence**)
messy — The text says that making the pie 'creates quite a bit of washing up if you're anything like me'. (2d)

5. (**1 mark**) It stops the base becoming soggy. (2b)

6. (**1 mark for a sensible answer with one piece of supporting evidence**)
e.g. Brian prefers the all-in-one-day method because he says people 'should definitely' do it if they have time.
(**2 marks for a sensible answer with two pieces of supporting evidence**)
e.g. Brian prefers the all-in-one-day method, as he says people 'should definitely' try it. He also says the method that splits the baking into two sessions is 'less satisfying', suggesting that he doesn't like it as much.
(**3 marks for a sensible answer with three pieces of supporting evidence**)
e.g. Brian prefers the all-in-one-day method because he says it removes the 'inconvenient waiting' involved in the other method, and that people 'should definitely' try it. He also calls the other method 'less satisfying', suggesting that he likes it less. (2d)

BONUS BRAINTEASER
e.g. Brian uses exclamation marks, such as when he says 'Let's go!' He also uses positive adjectives such as 'magnificent' and 'delicious' to describe his recipe.

Test 6 – Pages 37-39

1. (**1 mark**) His three listeners leaned forward eagerly (2d)

2. (**1 mark**) a holy man (2b)

3. (**1 mark for a sensible answer with one piece of supporting evidence**)
e.g. No, because they laugh at the sergeant-major when he talks about the spell.
(**2 marks for a sensible answer with two pieces of supporting evidence**)
e.g. No, because they laugh at the sergeant-major when he tells them about the spell. Mrs White asks 'did you really have the three wishes granted', suggesting she isn't sure that he is telling the truth. (2d)

4. (**1 mark for a sensible answer without supporting evidence**)

e.g. He didn't enjoy making his wishes.
(**2 marks for a sensible answer with supporting evidence**)
e.g. His 'blotchy face whitened' when he talked about his wishes. This suggests that he didn't enjoy making them. (2d)

5. (**1 mark for one sensible point**)
e.g. One of the Whites will have three wishes.
(**2 marks for two sensible points**)
e.g. A member of the White family will have three wishes. Something bad will happen to them because of the wishes. (2e)

BONUS BRAINTEASER
e.g. At the start of the text, Mrs White is curious about the paw, because she leans forward 'eagerly'. When she sees the paw, she seems disgusted, because she draws back from it with a 'grimace', but by the end of the story she is interested in it again because she 'persisted' in asking questions about it.

Puzzle – Page 40

The unscrambled sentences are:
After the stumps he passed the arguing ducks.
From the pond he went to see the bear.
He started off at the stumps.
He moved from the ducks to the pond.
The bear told him to go and hide in the hut.

You should have numbered the pictures like this:

Scoresheet Question – Page 41

TREE

Set C

Test 1 – Pages 42-44

1. (**1 mark**) Wet plants from the pond in her hair (2b)

2. (**1 mark for a sensible answer without supporting evidence**)
e.g. Zola is scared of the worms.
(**2 marks for a sensible answer with supporting evidence**)
e.g. Zola is scared of the worms because she 'darted' towards the toilets when she saw the boys playing with them. (2d)

3. (**1 mark**) The teacher isn't paying attention because she's marking work. (2b)

4. (**1 mark for both correct**)
catastrophe, calamity (2a)

5. (**1 mark for all correct**)
The class have a science lesson outside. ☐1☐
The narrator runs to the toilet. ☐4☐
Emre interferes with the narrator's plan. ☐3☐
Zola helps the narrator. ☐5☐
Some boys play with worms. ☐2☐ (2f)

6. (**1 mark for a sensible answer without supporting evidence**)
e.g. She was annoyed with Zola at the start of the text, but she is grateful to Zola at the end.
(**2 marks for a sensible answer with supporting evidence**)
e.g. The narrator is annoyed with Zola at the start of the text because she nudged the narrator into a pond. At the end of the text, she thinks Zola is selfless because she helps pick the worms out of the narrator's bag. (2h)

BONUS BRAINTEASER
e.g. The narrator might have learnt that sometimes people make mistakes and they deserve a second chance.

Test 2 – Pages 45-47

1. (**1 mark for a sensible answer**)
e.g. break into pieces (2a)

2. (**1 mark**) Because the peak viewing times are between 9th and 14th August. (2b)

3. (**1 mark**) They only have a small amount of light pollution. (2b)

Answers

4. (**1 mark for all correct**)
The meteor shower occurs every year. — True
The meteors are best seen before midnight. — False
Going to the countryside doesn't make a difference. — False
Meteors are also known as shooting stars. — True (2b)

5. (**1 mark**) It can take up to twenty minutes for their eyes to adjust to the darkness. (2b)

6. (**1 mark for one point without supporting evidence**)
e.g. Because it is best seen late at night.
(**2 marks for two points without supporting evidence OR for one point with supporting evidence**)
e.g. Because it is best seen 'after midnight', when most people sleep.
(**3 marks for two points with at least one piece of supporting evidence**)
e.g. People might miss it if they live in an 'urban area' because light pollution will make it hard to see the meteors. People could also miss it due to summer storms causing the view to be 'shrouded by clouds'. (2d)

BONUS BRAINTEASER
e.g. dazzling display, Amazing!, astonishing phenomenon

Test 3 – Pages 48-50

1. (**1 mark**) A place of worship (2b)

2. (**1 mark for a sensible answer**)
e.g. The text says that, out of Anne Boleyn, Lady Jane Grey and Elizabeth I, only Elizabeth 'escaped the executioner'. This shows that the other two died. (2d)

3. (**1 mark**) During the reign of Charles II. (2b)

4. (**1 mark**) allegedly (2a)

5. (**1 mark for all correct**)
The Tower will fall if the ravens fly away. — Opinion
The Tower is an impressive building. — Opinion
Four raven chicks hatched in 2019. — Fact

Beefeaters still guard the Tower of London. — Fact (2d)

6. (**1 mark for a sensible answer with one piece of supporting evidence**)
e.g. Yes, because the text says they are 'admired' as a symbol of the Tower of London.
(**2 marks for a sensible answer with two pieces of supporting evidence**)
e.g. Yes, because they 'inspire fondness' and are 'admired as an iconic symbol' of the Tower.
(**3 marks for a sensible answer with three pieces of supporting evidence**)
e.g. Most Londoners like the ravens because they 'inspire fondness' and are 'admired' as an iconic symbol of the Tower. However, some Londoners don't like them because bad behaviour by some ravens has 'harmed their reputation'. (2d)

BONUS BRAINTEASER
imposing, sinister, infamous, formidable, impressive

Test 4 – Pages 51-53

1. (**1 mark**) Nichol's heart sank (2f)

2. (**1 mark**) He thinks the water might be harmful. (2b)

3. (**1 mark**) hungry (2a)

4. (**1 mark for a sensible answer**)
e.g. No, because the text says he 'resigned himself' to it, which means he didn't really want to do it. (2d)

5. (**1 mark for a sensible answer without supporting evidence**)
e.g. Nichol dislikes the Dead Sea at the start of the story but he likes it at the end.
(**2 marks for a sensible answer with supporting evidence**)
e.g. Nichol is disappointed by the Dead Sea at first. He says 'We can go to the beach at home', which shows he doesn't think it's a special place. However, at the end of the story he likes the Dead Sea because he realises there aren't any 'menacing creatures' in it. (2h)

Answers

6. (**1 mark for one sensible point**)
e.g. Nichol will spend the morning in the Dead Sea.
(**2 marks for two sensible points**)
e.g. Nichol and his mum will spend the morning in the Dead Sea. Later, they will catch a flight home. (2e)

BONUS BRAINTEASER
leapt, fizzing, expectantly

Test 5 – Pages 54-56

1. (**1 mark for a sensible answer**)
e.g. Because the old inn was burnt down. (2d)

2. (**1 mark for two of the following**)
It suggests that the dragon was very big.
It suggests that the dragon was cruel.
It suggests that the dragon was frightening.
(2g)

3. (**1 mark for both correct**)
in a flash
immediately sprang into action (2a)

4. (**1 mark**) Failed feats (2c)

5. (**1 mark**) They are siblings. (2b)

6. (**1 mark for one point without supporting evidence**)
e.g. There was relief because Dolores and Donald made things worse.
(**2 marks for two points without supporting evidence OR for one point with supporting evidence**)
e.g. There was grief because the twins meant well when they tried to help, but there was relief because their actions made things worse.
(**3 marks for two points with at least one piece of supporting evidence**)
e.g. There was grief because Dolores and Donald 'earnestly sought' to meet people's needs. However, there was relief because the twins' attempts to help people were unsuccessful. For example, they tried to protect Farmer Olga's crops, but ended up destroying all of them. (2d)

BONUS BRAINTEASER
e.g. The Terrible Twins, A Destructive Duo, Memorable Deeds

Test 6 – Pages 57-59

1. (**1 mark for all correct**)
They are mainly used to see hidden objects.
— False
They have been around for over one hundred years. — True
Their mirrors reflect light at 360 degree angles. — False
They have been used to protect soldiers.
— True (2b)

2. (**1 mark for one sensible point**)
e.g. The text says that a periscope has 'endless uses'.
(**2 marks for two sensible points**)
e.g. The text says periscopes have 'endless uses' and that they are 'incredibly useful'. (2d)

3. (**1 mark**) crucial (2a)

4. (**1 mark**) They are often mounted on a base so they can turn through 360 degrees. (2b)

5. (**1 mark for three of the following**)
scissors, a pencil, mirrors, sticky tape (2b)

6. (**1 mark for all correct**)
exactly, carefully, perfectly (2g)

7. (**1 mark for a sensible answer**)
e.g. They both suggest that having a periscope is a step towards having a superpower. (2f)

BONUS BRAINTEASER
e.g. Because the numbered list makes it clear what order you should carry out the instructions in. It also separates each instruction, which makes them easier to follow.

Puzzles – Page 60

LEND, LENS, PENS, PINS, PIES, TIES

Scoresheet Question – Page 61

On safari, I saw animals, su**ch as e**lephants, lions and giraffes.
The five-letter word is **chase**.

Progress Chart

You've finished all the tests in the book — well done!

Now it's time to put your scores in here
and see how you've done.

	Set A	Set B	Set C
Test 1			
Test 2			
Test 3			
Test 4			
Test 5			
Test 6			
Total			

See if you're on target by checking your marks for each set in the table below.

Mark	
0-23	You're not quite there yet — keep going back over the questions you find tricky and you'll improve your reading skills in no time.
24-36	Good job! You're doing really well, but make sure you keep working on your weaker topics so that you're really ready for your test.
37-48	Give yourself a huge pat on the back — you're on track to ace your test! You're a reading star — well done!

This page may be photocopied